Unit 9
Assessment

Level 1

Blackline Masters

A Division of The McGraw·Hill Companies

Columbus, Ohio

www.sra4kids.com

SRA/McGraw-Hill

A Division of The **McGraw·Hill** *Companies*

Send all inquiries to:
SRA/McGraw-Hill
8787 Orion Place
Columbus, OH 43240-4027

Printed in the United States of America.

ISBN 0-07-571371-3

6 7 8 9 MAZ 07 06 05

Table of Contents

Lesson Assessments

Lesson 2: My Brother Is Afraid of Just About Everything. 2

Lesson 3: Little Miss Muffet 6

Lesson 4: Goblin Story 10

Lesson 5: Strange Bumps 14

Lesson 6: Clyde Monster 18

Lesson 7: The Cat and the Mice 22

Lesson 8: Ira Sleeps Over. 26

Lesson 9: Something Is There 30

Lesson 10: The Three Billy Goats Gruff. 34

Lessons I-II: Spelling Pretest and Final Tests 38

End of Unit Assessments

Multiple Choice Assessments

Comprehension Assessment 48

Spelling Assessment 50

Vocabulary Assessment 51

Grammar, Usage, and Mechanics Assessment 52

Writer's Craft Assessment 53

Teacher Directed Assessments

Oral Fluency Assessment 54

Listening Assessment 55

Writing Prompt 56

UNIT 9 • Being Afraid • **Lesson 2**

My Brother Is Afraid of Just About Everything

Read the following questions carefully. Then completely fill in the bubble of each correct answer. You may look back at the story to find the answer to each of the questions.

1. Where does the little brother go during thunderstorms?
   - Ⓐ into his closet
   - Ⓑ behind the couch
   - Ⓒ under the bed

2. What is the big sister afraid of?
   - Ⓐ mice
   - Ⓑ dogs
   - Ⓒ spiders

3. The little brother is afraid of the
   - Ⓐ dishwasher
   - Ⓑ lawnmower
   - Ⓒ vacuum cleaner

Read the following question carefully. Use a complete sentence to answer the question.

4. What does little brother do when his sister's friends talk to him?

_____

Read the following questions carefully. Then completely fill in the bubble of each correct answer.

5. What is true about the mailman in this story?
   - Ⓐ He has a beard.
   - Ⓑ He is friendly.
   - Ⓒ He has a bicycle.

6. How do the big sister's friends feel about her little brother?
   - Ⓐ They think he is a pest.
   - Ⓑ They think he is funny.
   - Ⓒ They think he is cute.

Read the following question carefully. Use a complete sentence to answer the question.

7. What does the big sister learn about being afraid?

_____

_____

Personal Response Write about something that you used to be afraid of but aren't afraid of anymore.

_____

_____

Vocabulary

Read the following questions carefully. Then completely fill in the bubble of each correct answer.

1. The little brother buried his face in his big sister's stomach. In this sentence, **buried** means
   - Ⓐ hid
   - Ⓑ yelled
   - Ⓒ cried

2. Most children think trains are pretty exciting. When something is **exciting**, it is
   - Ⓐ real
   - Ⓑ fun
   - Ⓒ dumb

3. The little brother in this story is scared about a lot of things. Another word for **scared** is
   - Ⓐ angry
   - Ⓑ happy
   - Ⓒ afraid

4. The little brother's mouth **quivered**. This means the little brother's mouth
   - Ⓐ shook
   - Ⓑ smiled
   - Ⓒ opened

Phonics Review

Fill in the bubble of the word that fits in the blank and is spelled correctly.

1. I can't untie this _____.

   ○ knot   ○ not   ○ hnot

2. You can _____ here.

   ○ sta   ○ stay   ○ stae

3. What is the _____ of that girl?

   ○ nam   ○ naim   ○ name

4. The workers were _____.

   ○ pad   ○ paid   ○ payd

5. John is _____ to run far.

   ○ ayble   ○ aeble   ○ able

6. We heard a _____ on the door.

   ○ knock   ○ nock   ○ wnock

UNIT 9 Being Afraid • **Lesson 3**

Little Miss Muffet

Read the following questions carefully. Then completely fill in the bubble of each correct answer. You may look back at the story to find the answer to each of the questions.

1. What was Miss Muffet doing when the spider came along?

   Ⓐ She was playing outside.

   Ⓑ She was singing a song.

   Ⓒ She was having a meal.

2. You can tell that Miss Muffet is afraid of

   Ⓐ spiders

   Ⓑ dogs

   Ⓒ trains

Read the following question carefully. Use a complete sentence to answer the question.

3. Where did Miss Muffet probably go at the end of the poem?

   _____

   _____

Read the following questions carefully. Then completely fill in the bubble of each correct answer.

4. What is this story mostly about?
   - Ⓐ a girl who likes nature
   - Ⓑ a spider who buys curds
   - Ⓒ a girl who gets frightened

5. What kind of story is this?
   - Ⓐ make-believe
   - Ⓑ true
   - Ⓒ sad

6. Before she sees the spider, Miss Muffet is
   - Ⓐ feeling rather lonely
   - Ⓑ worrying about things
   - Ⓒ eating her food

Read the following question carefully. Use a complete sentence to answer the question.

7. What makes "Little Miss Muffet" a nursery rhyme?

_____

_____

Personal Response Do you think the spider frightened Miss Muffet on purpose? Why?

_____

Vocabulary

Read the following questions carefully. Then completely fill in the bubble of each correct answer.

1. A **tuffet** is like a
   - Ⓐ dish
   - Ⓑ food
   - Ⓒ pillow

2. **Curds** are like
   - Ⓐ pieces of bread
   - Ⓑ pieces of meat
   - Ⓒ pieces of cheese

3. **Whey** is like
   - Ⓐ cereal
   - Ⓑ milk
   - Ⓒ juice

4. To **frighten** someone means to
   - Ⓐ tease that person
   - Ⓑ jump on that person
   - Ⓒ scare that person

Phonics Review

Completely fill in the bubble of each correct answer.

1. ○ gren   ○ green   ○ grean

2. ○ shee   ○ she   ○ shy

3. ○ seat   ○ set   ○ sete

4. ○ her   ○ hier   ○ here

5. ○ cooke   ○ cookie   ○ cookee

6. ○ vere   ○ veree   ○ very

7. ○ pet   ○ pat   ○ pit

8. ○ mup   ○ map   ○ mep

UNIT 9 Being Afraid • **Lesson 4**

We're Going on a Bear Hunt

Read the following questions carefully. Then completely fill in the bubble of each correct answer. You may look back at the story to find the answer to each of the questions.

1. When they came to the grass, they went
   - Ⓐ over it
   - Ⓑ through it
   - Ⓒ under it

2. When they went through the forest, the noise they made was
   - Ⓐ sticky wicky
   - Ⓑ push woosh
   - Ⓒ stumble trip

3. What did the bear have?
   - Ⓐ a big furry tail
   - Ⓑ a warm nose
   - Ⓒ goggly eyes

Read the following question carefully. Use a complete sentence to answer the question.

4. What was the cave like?

_____

Read the following questions carefully. Then completely fill in the bubble of each correct answer.

5. Why did they have to come back downstairs?
   Ⓐ to see the bear
   Ⓑ to find the dog
   Ⓒ to shut the door

6. What did they go through first?
   Ⓐ a river
   Ⓑ a field of grass
   Ⓒ a forest

7. What did they think they would do?
   Ⓐ catch a bear
   Ⓑ play with a bear
   Ⓒ chase a bear

Read the following question carefully. Use a complete sentence to answer the question.

8. What will they never do again?

_____

_____

Personal Response Write about a time you went on an adventure. Did it turn out the way you thought it would?

Vocabulary

Read the following questions carefully. Then completely fill in the bubble of each correct answer.

1. If a room is **gloomy,** it is
   - Ⓐ dirty
   - Ⓑ large
   - Ⓒ dark

2. When you **tiptoe,** you
   - Ⓐ walk on your toes
   - Ⓑ step on someone's toes
   - Ⓒ hurt your toe

3. A **wavy** line is
   - Ⓐ straight
   - Ⓑ curvy
   - Ⓒ thick

4. A place that is **narrow** is
   - Ⓐ filled with people
   - Ⓑ not very wide
   - Ⓒ too dark to see

Phonics Review

Fill in the bubble of the word that fits in the blank and is spelled correctly.

1. Dan reads _____ day.
    ○ evere   ○ every   ○ everee

2. Are you _____ that pen?
    ○ using   ○ uesing   ○ uusing

3. Jen rode a _____ on the path.
    ○ mul   ○ muel   ○ mule

4. The _____ sounds nice.
    ○ moosic   ○ mewsic   ○ music

5. Bill has a _____ toys.
    ○ few   ○ fu   ○ fue

6. Mom filled the tank with _____.
    ○ fuul   ○ fuel   ○ fewl

UNIT 9 • Being Afraid • **Lesson 5**

Strange Bumps

Read the following questions carefully. Then completely fill in the bubble of each correct answer. You may look back at the story to find the answer to each of the questions.

1. What is Owl afraid the bumps will do while he is asleep?

   Ⓐ escape

   Ⓑ explode

   Ⓒ grow bigger

2. Where does Owl decide to sleep?

   Ⓐ on a bench in his kitchen

   Ⓑ on the couch in his living room

   Ⓒ in his chair by the fire

Read the following question carefully. Use a complete sentence to answer the question.

3. What happens to the bumps when Owl pulls off his covers?

   _____

   _____

Strange Bumps (*continued*)

Read the following questions carefully. Then completely fill in the bubble of each correct answer.

4. Which of these best describes Owl?

Ⓐ smart

Ⓑ silly

Ⓒ kind

5. Why do the bumps move?

Ⓐ because Owl is watching them

Ⓑ because Owl is scaring them

Ⓒ because Owl moves his feet

Read the following question carefully. Use a complete sentence to answer the question.

6. What were the bumps that Owl saw?

_____

_____

Personal Response Write about a time you felt silly about something you thought was true.

_____

_____

_____

_____

Vocabulary

Read the following questions carefully. Then completely fill in the bubble of each correct answer.

1. Owl says it would not be pleasant if the bumps grew bigger. **Pleasant** means about the same as
   Ⓐ scary
   Ⓑ warm
   Ⓒ nice

2. A **crash** happens when something
   Ⓐ disappears
   Ⓑ breaks
   Ⓒ gets fixed

3. There was a bang when the bed came falling down. A **bang** is a
   Ⓐ pretty song
   Ⓑ loud noise
   Ⓒ strong wind

4. Another word for **bump** is
   Ⓐ shout
   Ⓑ blanket
   Ⓒ lump

Phonics Review

Fill in the bubble of the answer you think is correct.

LESSON ASSESSMENT

1. bl____
  ○ u   ○ ue   ○ oo

2. h____t
  ○ uu   ○ ue   ○ oo

3. c____
  ○ ue   ○ o   ○ u

4. st____
  ○ ew   ○ u   ○ uw

5. m____d
  ○ o   ○ oo   ○ uu

6. ____sed
  ○ uu   ○ ue   ○ u

UNIT 9 Being Afraid • **Lesson 6**

Clyde Monster

Read the following questions carefully. Then completely fill in the bubble of each correct answer. You may look back at the story to find the answer to each of the questions.

1. What does Clyde do during the day?
   - Ⓐ He plays in the forest.
   - Ⓑ He hides in his cave.
   - Ⓒ He digs holes in the ground.

2. Where is Clyde supposed to sleep at night?
   - Ⓐ on his cot
   - Ⓑ in his castle
   - Ⓒ in his cave

3. What is Clyde afraid of?
   - Ⓐ dogs
   - Ⓑ loud noises
   - Ⓒ people

Read the following question carefully. Use a complete sentence to answer the question.

4. What does Clyde's father show him?

_____

_____

Read the following questions carefully. Then completely fill in the bubble of each correct answer.

5. According to the story, what do a lot of monsters do?
  - Ⓐ breathe fire at lakes
  - Ⓑ listen to their parents' music
  - Ⓒ build fires inside caves

6. Why does Clyde's father breathe fire into the cave?
  - Ⓐ to scare out anyone who might be hiding there
  - Ⓑ to get the cave warm before Clyde goes to bed
  - Ⓒ to show Clyde there are no people in the cave

Read the following question carefully. Use a complete sentence to answer the question.

7. What does Clyde ask his parents to do when he goes to bed?

_____

_____

Personal Response What do you do to feel safe at night?

_____

_____

_____

Vocabulary

Read the following questions carefully. Then completely fill in the bubble of each correct answer.

1. Clyde played in the forest doing typical monster things. **Typical** means

   Ⓐ usual

   Ⓑ funny

   Ⓒ grown-up

2. Doing a **somersault** is like

   Ⓐ jumping up and down

   Ⓑ flipping over

   Ⓒ balancing on one foot

3. A **clumsy** person

   Ⓐ has a lot of accidents

   Ⓑ is very good at sports

   Ⓒ has a lot of friends

4. Clyde's father **snorted**. This means Clyde's father

   Ⓐ worried about Clyde

   Ⓑ laughed very hard

   Ⓒ made a noise through his nose

Phonics Review

Fill in the bubble of the word that fits in the blank and is spelled correctly.

1. Let's take a _____ walk.
   ○ kick   ○ cick   ○ quick

2. When will you come _____?
   ○ back   ○ bac   ○ baqu

3. That is a nice _____.
   ○ kar   ○ car   ○ ckar

4. Please be _____.
   ○ cwiet   ○ quiet   ○ kwiet

5. The story is about a _____.
   ○ king   ○ quing   ○ cing

6. Did you _____ the door?
   ○ loc   ○ loqu   ○ lock

UNIT 9 Being Afraid • **Lesson 7**

The Cat and the Mice

Read the following questions carefully. Then completely fill in the bubble of each correct answer. You may look back at the story to find the answer to each of the questions.

1. What is the mouse family's problem?
   - Ⓐ A cat keeps chasing them.
   - Ⓑ There are mousetraps all around them.
   - Ⓒ They can't find enough food.

2. What is the smallest mouse's idea?
   - Ⓐ to get a dog
   - Ⓑ to hang a bell on the cat's neck
   - Ⓒ to look for a new home

3. Who does not like the smallest mouse's idea?
   - Ⓐ the father mouse
   - Ⓑ the biggest mouse
   - Ⓒ the oldest mouse

Read the following question carefully. Use a complete sentence to answer the question.

4. What does the oldest mouse ask the others?

   _____

   _____

Read the following questions carefully. Then completely fill in the bubble of each correct answer.

5. Why is the cat chasing the family of mice?
- Ⓐ because it wants to play
- Ⓑ because it is hungry
- Ⓒ because it is lonely

6. Why didn't anyone answer the oldest mouse's question?
- Ⓐ They are too scared.
- Ⓑ They are not listening.
- Ⓒ They are too angry.

Read the following question carefully. Use a complete sentence to answer the question.

7. How would the bell help the mice?

_____

_____

Personal Response Which mouse do you think was the smartest? Why do you think this?

_____

_____

_____

Vocabulary

Read the following questions carefully. Then completely fill in the bubble of each correct answer.

1. To be **clever** means to be
   Ⓐ strong
   Ⓑ smart
   Ⓒ pretty

2. The mouse family squealed in excitement. In this sentence, to **squeal** means
   Ⓐ make a happy noise
   Ⓑ make a scared noise
   Ⓒ make a hurt noise

3. The mice are excited when they hear the idea. When you are **excited** about something, it is
   Ⓐ easy to keep quiet
   Ⓑ not very interesting
   Ⓒ hard to wait for

4. **Chase** means about the same as
   Ⓐ run after
   Ⓑ like
   Ⓒ forget about

Phonics Review

Fill in the bubble of the answer you think is correct.

1. m____se
- ○ ou
- ○ oo
- ○ oi

2. h____
- ○ ar
- ○ er
- ○ eer

3. c____
- ○ oo
- ○ ow
- ○ au

4. d____t
- ○ ar
- ○ or
- ○ ir

5. b____n
- ○ ur
- ○ ar
- ○ or

6. th____d
- ○ er
- ○ or
- ○ ir

UNIT 9 Being Afraid • **Lesson 8**

Ira Sleeps Over

Read the following questions carefully. Then completely fill in the bubble of each correct answer. You may look back at the story to find the answer to each of the questions.

1. Why is Ira so excited at the start of the story?
   - Ⓐ He gets a brand-new toy.
   - Ⓑ He meets someone new.
   - Ⓒ He gets to do something new.

2. Ira's sister asks him if
   - Ⓐ he is going to have fun at Reggie's
   - Ⓑ he will bring his teddy bear to Reggie's
   - Ⓒ he has seen Reggie's junk collection

3. Which of these is true about Ira's sister?
   - Ⓐ She thinks Ira is cute.
   - Ⓑ She takes care of Ira.
   - Ⓒ She likes to tease Ira.

Read the following question carefully. Use a complete sentence to answer the question.

4. What kind of plans does Reggie have for the evening?

_____

Read the following questions carefully. Then completely fill in the bubble of each correct answer.

5. This story is mostly about
  Ⓐ why kids like teddy bears
  Ⓑ a boy who sleeps over at a friend's house
  Ⓒ two boys who are friends

6. Why doesn't Ira take his teddy bear to Reggie's house?
  Ⓐ He asks his sister to take care of it.
  Ⓑ He is not worried about being afraid.
  Ⓒ He thinks Reggie will laugh at him.

Read the following question carefully. Use a complete sentence to answer the question.

7. When does Ira decide it is okay to go and get his teddy bear?

_____

_____

Personal Response What do you have that is like Ira's teddy bear?

_____

_____

Vocabulary

Read the following questions carefully. Then completely fill in the bubble of each correct answer.

1. A **problem** is something that
   Ⓐ is easy to understand
   Ⓑ makes you really happy
   Ⓒ you have to figure out

2. A **teddy bear** is
   Ⓐ a toy bear
   Ⓑ a mother bear
   Ⓒ a young bear

3. A **magnifying glass** makes things look
   Ⓐ smaller
   Ⓑ bigger
   Ⓒ funnier

4. What is a **collection**?
   Ⓐ a scary story
   Ⓑ a game you play with two people
   Ⓒ a bunch of things that go together

Phonics Review

Fill in the bubble of the word that fits in the blank and is spelled correctly.

1. This is a _____ bus.

    ○ slo   ○ sloo   ○ slow

2. My friend has a _____.

    ○ pone   ○ pony   ○ poni

3. Grandma tells good _____

    ○ stories   ○ storees   ○ storieys

4. It will _____ soon.

    ○ sno   ○ snoa   ○ snow

5. The _____ is very blue today.

    ○ sky   ○ ski   ○ skiy

6. That bird _____ fast.

    ○ flyys   ○ flies   ○ flis

UNIT 9 Being Afraid • **Lesson 9**

Something Is There

Read the following questions carefully. Then completely fill in the bubble of each correct answer. You may look back at the story to find the answer to each of the questions.

1. What is the something on the stair?
   - Ⓐ a mouse
   - Ⓑ a cat
   - Ⓒ The poem does not say.

2. Where is the something going?
   - Ⓐ up the stair
   - Ⓑ down the stair
   - Ⓒ under the stair

3. The something is stepping
   - Ⓐ quickly
   - Ⓑ slowly
   - Ⓒ loudly

Read the following question carefully. Use a complete sentence to answer the question.

4. How is this poem supposed to make you feel?

   _____

   _____

Read the following questions carefully. Then completely fill in the bubble of each correct answer.

5. In this poem, which word is repeated?
Ⓐ stair
Ⓑ slinkety-sly
Ⓒ down

6. This poem is most like
Ⓐ a scary story
Ⓑ an animal story
Ⓒ a new game

Read the following question carefully. Use a complete sentence to answer the question.

7. Why can't the children see what the something is?

_____

_____

Personal Response How do you feel when you hear a strange noise? After you find out what the noise is, then how do you feel?

_____

_____

_____

Vocabulary

Read the following questions carefully. Then completely fill in the bubble of each correct answer.

1. What does the word **slinkety-sly** tell you about the something on the stair?
   - Ⓐ how it moves
   - Ⓑ what it looks like
   - Ⓒ who it is

2. Which of these describes **stairs**?
   - Ⓐ a long and straight path
   - Ⓑ steps that go up and down
   - Ⓒ windows that you see through

3. The **stepping** done in this poem is most like
   - Ⓐ dancing
   - Ⓑ running
   - Ⓒ creeping

4. What is the opposite of **coming**?
   - Ⓐ staying
   - Ⓑ going
   - Ⓒ playing

Phonics Review

Fill in the bubble of the answer you think is correct.

1. c____k

○ oo   ○ ou   ○ oa

2. m____n

○ o   ○ oo   ○ ou

3. st____p

○ oo   ○ oi   ○ o

4. m____st

○ oa   ○ o   ○ oo

5. gl____

○ o   ○ oe   ○ ow

6. c____t

○ oa   ○ oe   ○ oo

Name _____ Date _____ Score _____

LESSON ASSESSMENT

The Three Billy Goats Gruff

Read the following questions carefully. Then completely fill in the bubble of each correct answer. You may look back at the story to find the answer to each of the questions.

1. Why did the billy goats want to cross the river?
   - Ⓐ to find some other goats to play with
   - Ⓑ to look for a new home
   - Ⓒ to eat the tall, green grass

2. The first two billy goats got across because
   - Ⓐ they ran fast so the troll couldn't catch them
   - Ⓑ they tiptoed so the troll didn't hear them
   - Ⓒ they told the troll to wait for their brother

3. The billy goats could trick the troll because
   - Ⓐ the troll was sleepy
   - Ⓑ the troll was greedy
   - Ⓒ the troll was afraid

Read the following question carefully. Use a complete sentence to answer the question.

4. What did the biggest billy goat do to the troll?

   _____

   _____

Read the following questions carefully. Then completely fill in the bubble of each correct answer.

5. Which of these shows this is a make-believe story?
   Ⓐ Goats do not talk.
   Ⓑ Goats do not go over bridges.
   Ⓒ Goats do not butt things.

6. The troll in this story is
   Ⓐ playful
   Ⓑ unfriendly
   Ⓒ smart

Read the following question carefully. Use a complete sentence to answer the question.

7. Did the first two billy goats want the troll to eat their brother? Explain what you mean.

_____

_____

Personal Response Did you like this story? Why or why not?

_____

_____

Vocabulary

Read the following questions carefully. Then completely fill in the bubble of each correct answer.

1. A **meadow** is
   - Ⓐ a field of grass and flowers
   - Ⓑ a field of very tall corn
   - Ⓒ a field of trees and bushes

2. A **troll** is a
   - Ⓐ friendly goat farmer
   - Ⓑ make-believe monster
   - Ⓒ mean and ugly goat

3. Another word for **greedy** is
   - Ⓐ lonely
   - Ⓑ kind
   - Ⓒ selfish

4. The troll's eyes are as big as saucers. **Saucers** are
   - Ⓐ pebbles
   - Ⓑ dishes
   - Ⓒ peas

Phonics Review

Fill in the bubble of the word that fits in the blank and is spelled correctly.

1. My mother cut my _____.
   ○ har   ○ hair   ○ hear

2. Do you like to _____?
   ○ sing   ○ sind   ○ sinp

3. Ben hurt his _____.
   ○ eer   ○ ere   ○ ear

4. Can I have _____ milk, please?
   ○ mor   ○ more   ○ moor

5. Dad went to the _____.
   ○ bank   ○ bangk   ○ banh

6. The _____ feels good.
   ○ fir   ○ fiir   ○ fire

My Brother Is Afraid of Just

UNIT 9 **Being Afraid • Lessons 1–2** *About Everything*

Spelling Pretest: Review Sound Spellings

Fold this page back on the dotted line. Take the Pretest. Then correct any word you misspelled by crossing out the word and rewriting it next to the incorrect spelling.

1. _____

2. _____

3. _____

4. _____

5. _____

6. _____

1. those

2. way

3. train

4. knees

5. face

6. card

My Brother Is Afraid of Just

UNIT 9 Being Afraid • **Lessons 1–2** *About Everything*

Spelling Final Test: Review Sound Spellings

Look at the <u>underlined</u> words. Find the one that is spelled wrong. Fill in its circle.

1. Ⓐ He got a <u>card</u> for his birthday.
   Ⓑ Show me the <u>way</u> to the school.
   Ⓒ The <u>train</u> stops at the station.
   Ⓓ All the <u>underlined</u> words are spelled right.

2. Ⓕ We want <u>those</u> cans of pop.
   Ⓖ Your <u>nees</u> let your legs bend.
   Ⓗ Your <u>face</u> has lips, a nose, and eyes.
   Ⓙ All the <u>underlined</u> words are spelled right.

3. Ⓐ Which <u>wae</u> do we turn?
   Ⓑ A <u>train</u> runs on tracks.
   Ⓒ Are <u>those</u> your books?
   Ⓓ All the <u>underlined</u> words are spelled right.

4. Ⓕ Jeff wants this baseball <u>card</u>.
   Ⓖ He fell on his <u>knees</u>.
   Ⓗ A clown puts paint on her <u>fase</u>.
   Ⓙ All the <u>underlined</u> words are spelled right.

5. Ⓐ My dad rides the <u>trayn</u> to work.
   Ⓑ She was happy all the <u>way</u> home.
   Ⓒ Do you want to eat <u>those</u> bananas?
   Ⓓ All the <u>underlined</u> words are spelled right.

UNIT 9 **Being Afraid • Lessons 3–4** *Little Miss Muffet*
We're Going on a Bear Hunt

Spelling Pretest: Review Sound Spellings

Fold this page back on the dotted line. Take the
Pretest. Then correct any word you misspelled by
crossing out the word and rewriting it next to the
incorrect spelling.

1. _____

2. _____

3. _____

4. _____

5. _____

6. _____

1. beg

2. clap

3. silly

4. few

5. deep

6. trip

Name _____ Date _____ Score _____

Spelling Final Test: Review Sound Spellings

Look at the <u>underlined</u> words. Find the one that is spelled wrong. Fill in its circle.

1.
   Ⓐ A <u>few</u> flowers are blooming.
   Ⓑ She wrote a <u>silly</u> story.
   Ⓒ The water in the lake is <u>deep</u>.
   Ⓓ All the <u>underlined</u> words are spelled right.

2.
   Ⓕ My dog likes to <u>begg</u> for food.
   Ⓖ Watch your step or you might <u>trip</u>.
   Ⓗ The <u>silly</u> song made me smile.
   Ⓙ All the <u>underlined</u> words are spelled right.

3.
   Ⓐ The clown made a <u>sille</u> face.
   Ⓑ I <u>beg</u> your pardon.
   Ⓒ The cat ran in the <u>deep</u> hole.
   Ⓓ All the <u>underlined</u> words are spelled right.

4.
   Ⓕ Bob went on a <u>trip</u> to Washington.
   Ⓖ We <u>clap</u> our hands to the beat of the song.
   Ⓗ A <u>fue</u> books are on the desk.
   Ⓙ All the <u>underlined</u> words are spelled right.

5.
   Ⓐ We have a <u>few</u> pets at our house.
   Ⓑ Oceans are <u>dep</u> and salty.
   Ⓒ He told a <u>silly</u> joke.
   Ⓓ All the <u>underlined</u> words are spelled right.

UNIT 9 Being Afraid • **Lessons 5–6** *Strange Bumps*
Clyde Monster

Spelling Pretest: Review Sound Spellings

Fold this page back on the dotted line. Take the Pretest. Then correct any word you misspelled by crossing out the word and rewriting it next to the incorrect spelling.

1. _____

2. _____

3. _____

4. _____

5. _____

6. _____

1. unit

2. quit

3. grew

4. tube

5. soon

6. quick

Spelling Final Test: Review Sound Spellings

Look at the <u>underlined</u> words. Find the one that is spelled wrong. Fill in its circle.

1. Ⓐ It will be dark <u>soon</u>.
   Ⓑ A <u>toob</u> of first-aid cream is in the kit.
   Ⓒ Susan's kitten <u>grew</u> to be a big cat.
   Ⓓ All the <u>underlined</u> words are spelled right.

2. Ⓕ Which spelling <u>unit</u> did you like the most?
   Ⓖ Dad made a <u>quick</u> trip to the store.
   Ⓗ My favorite TV show starts <u>soon</u>.
   Ⓙ All the <u>underlined</u> words are spelled right.

3. Ⓐ He only has time to tell a <u>kwick</u> story.
   Ⓑ You must <u>quit</u> chewing gum at school.
   Ⓒ She <u>grew</u> her hair long over the summer.
   Ⓓ All the <u>underlined</u> words are spelled right.

4. Ⓕ I <u>kwit</u> the soccer team.
   Ⓖ You must go to bed <u>soon</u>.
   Ⓗ Hand cream comes in a <u>tube</u>.
   Ⓙ All the <u>underlined</u> words are spelled right.

5. Ⓐ He must be <u>kwick</u> to win the race.
   Ⓑ The flower <u>grew</u> very tall.
   Ⓒ We learned about fish in our science <u>unit</u>.
   Ⓓ All the <u>underlined</u> words are spelled right.

The Cat and the Mice
UNIT 9 Being Afraid • **Lessons 7–8** *Ira Sleeps Over*

Spelling Pretest: Review Sound Spellings

Fold this page back on the dotted line. Take the Pretest. Then correct any word you misspelled by crossing out the word and rewriting it next to the incorrect spelling.

1. _____

2. _____

3. _____

4. _____

5. _____

6. _____

1. throw

2. dirt

3. dry

4. clown

5. story

6. out

Spelling Final Test: Review Sound Spellings

Look at the <u>underlined</u> words. Find the one that is spelled wrong. Fill in its circle.

1. Ⓐ We put <u>dirt</u> in the flowerpots.
   Ⓑ I will hang the towel to <u>dry</u> on the line.
   Ⓒ Bob told us a funny <u>story</u>.
   Ⓓ All the <u>underlined</u> words are spelled right.

2. Ⓕ Sara took her book <u>out</u> of her desk.
   Ⓖ He can <u>throe</u> a ball far.
   Ⓗ The <u>clown</u> had a big, red nose.
   Ⓙ All the <u>underlined</u> words are spelled right.

3. Ⓐ I will sweep the <u>durt</u> away from the door.
   Ⓑ It is time to get <u>out</u> of bed.
   Ⓒ My mom loves to read me a <u>story</u>.
   Ⓓ All the <u>underlined</u> words are spelled right.

4. Ⓕ The <u>clown</u> wore big shoes.
   Ⓖ The ground is <u>dry</u> and dusty.
   Ⓗ We went <u>owt</u> for dinner last night.
   Ⓙ All the <u>underlined</u> words are spelled right.

5. Ⓐ The <u>cloun</u> has a funny hat.
   Ⓑ Which <u>story</u> is your favorite?
   Ⓒ Do not <u>throw</u> stones.
   Ⓓ All the <u>underlined</u> words are spelled right.

UNIT 9 Being Afraid • **Lessons 9–11** *Something is There*
The Three Billy Goats Gruff

Spelling Pretest: Review Sound Spellings

Fold this page back on the dotted line. Take the Pretest. Then correct any word you misspelled by crossing out the word and rewriting it next to the incorrect spelling.

1. _____

2. _____

3. _____

4. _____

5. _____

6. _____

1. law

2. sting

3. fling

4. fawn

5. stair

6. roar

Something is There
UNIT 9 Being Afraid • **Lessons 9–11** *The Three Billy Goats Gruff*

Spelling Final Test: Review Sound Spellings

Look at the <u>underlined</u> words. Find the one that is spelled wrong. Fill in its circle.

1. Ⓐ We are not allowed to <u>fling</u> bits of mud in the air.
   Ⓑ It is against the <u>law</u> to steal.
   Ⓒ The man stood on the <u>stair</u>.
   Ⓓ All the <u>underlined</u> words are spelled right.

2. Ⓕ The lion let out a big, loud <u>rore</u>.
   Ⓖ We saw a <u>fawn</u> and a mother deer in a field.
   Ⓗ The smoke makes my eyes <u>sting</u>.
   Ⓙ All the <u>underlined</u> words are spelled right.

3. Ⓐ Bob went to <u>law</u> school.
   Ⓑ It is OK to <u>fling</u> small stones into the lake.
   Ⓒ A <u>stayr</u> is made of many steps.
   Ⓓ All the <u>underlined</u> words are spelled right.

4. Ⓕ The loud <u>roar</u> came from the hungry bear.
   Ⓖ Bees can <u>sting</u> when they are mad.
   Ⓗ A <u>lau</u> is a special rule.
   Ⓙ All the <u>underlined</u> words are spelled right.

5. Ⓐ We saw the toy on the bottom <u>stair</u>.
   Ⓑ The baby likes to <u>fling</u> its food into the air.
   Ⓒ A baby deer is called a <u>faun</u>.
   Ⓓ All the <u>underlined</u> words are spelled right.

UNIT 9 Being Afraid

Comprehension Assessment

Read the story silently. Then answer the questions about the story.

Going Fishing

Jerry woke up slowly. Today, he was going to do something new. Jerry, Mom, and Dad were going to the lake. They would go fishing. The problem was, Jerry was a little afraid of the water.

For a minute, Jerry stayed in bed. He thought about being in a boat. Then he slid out of bed and got dressed. He ran down the stairs to the kitchen.

"Are we still going to the lake?" asked Jerry.

"As soon as you have breakfast," answered Mom. She fixed Jerry cereal and a glass of juice. Mom and Dad reminded Jerry that he knew how to swim. They were sure he would have fun at the lake.

After breakfast, Jerry helped Dad put things in the car. Mom cleaned up and made lunch. Soon they were on their way.

When they got to the lake, Jerry was surprised. His cousin, Tina, was already there. So were Aunt Betsy and Uncle Ned. Aunt Betsy gave Jerry a hug. Uncle Ned pinched his nose.

Tina was about the same age as Jerry. He was glad she and her parents were here. Now he didn't feel so afraid. In fact, he was pretty excited.

END OF UNIT ASSESSMENT
Multiple Choice

Now read the following questions carefully. Then completely fill in the bubble of the correct answer.

1. Where does this story begin?

   Ⓐ at the lake

   Ⓑ in the family kitchen

   Ⓒ in Jerry's room

2. What is this story mostly about?

   Ⓐ why fishing is fun

   Ⓑ a family trip to a lake

   Ⓒ eating breakfast

3. Which of these is true about Jerry?

   Ⓐ He knows how to swim.

   Ⓑ He will learn how to swim at the lake.

   Ⓒ He doesn't know how to swim.

Read the following questions carefully. Answer each question with a complete sentence.

4. What helped Jerry to be less afraid?

   _____

   _____

5. How did Jerry change from the beginning of the story to the end?

   _____

   _____

END OF UNIT ASSESSMENT
Multiple Choice/Short Answer

UNIT 9 Being Afraid

Spelling Assessment

Look at the underlined words. Find the one that is spelled wrong. Fill in its circle.

1. Ⓐ Could I have one of those apples?
   Ⓑ We will clap when the team scores.
   Ⓒ I scraped my nees.
   Ⓓ He grew two inches.

2. Ⓕ That is a wonderful story.
   Ⓖ May I let the dog out?
   Ⓗ The ground is dry.
   Ⓙ That cloun is funny.

3. Ⓐ I got dert on my pants.
   Ⓑ Please throw the ball to me.
   Ⓒ You are a quick runner.
   Ⓓ Don't trip on the big branch!

4. Ⓕ She climbed the stair carefully.
   Ⓖ He will fling the ball to Mike.
   Ⓗ Sune it will be recess time.
   Ⓙ That is a silly face!

5. Ⓐ A bee can sting.
   Ⓑ The fawn drank water from the stream.
   Ⓒ That lake is dep!
   Ⓓ Which way should we turn?

END OF UNIT ASSESSMENT
Multiple Choice

UNIT 9 Being Afraid

Vocabulary Assessment

Use the sentence to figure out the meaning of the underlined word. Then choose the answer that best shows what the underlined word means.

SAMPLE

After not eating all day, I'm <u>famished</u>. **Famished means—**
- Ⓐ purple
- Ⓑ happy
- Ⓒ hungry
- Ⓓ strong

1. The <u>cave</u> was deep and dark. **A cave is a—**
   - Ⓐ hole
   - Ⓑ hill
   - Ⓒ animal
   - Ⓓ park

2. We heard the dog <u>howl</u> loudly at the moon. **Howl means—**
   - Ⓕ to jump
   - Ⓖ to cry out
   - Ⓗ to look
   - Ⓙ to love

3. The toy <u>snapped</u> in half when I stepped on it. **Snapped means—**
   - Ⓐ bent
   - Ⓑ broke
   - Ⓒ dark
   - Ⓓ cry

4. Elephants are big and <u>tough</u>. **Tough means—**
   - Ⓕ smooth
   - Ⓖ hairy
   - Ⓗ strong
   - Ⓙ soft

5. The <u>clumsy</u> lamb did not walk very well. **Clumsy means—**
   - Ⓐ awkward
   - Ⓑ baby
   - Ⓒ small
   - Ⓓ mad

END OF UNIT ASSESSMENT
Multiple Choice

UNIT 9   Being Afraid

Language: Grammar, Usage, and Mechanics Assessment

Fill in the circle next to the word that best completes each sentence.

1. I live in a white _____.
   - Ⓐ shoe
   - Ⓑ house
   - Ⓒ houses

2. My brother has _____ hair.
   - Ⓕ brown
   - Ⓖ slow
   - Ⓗ fast

3. ____ is a tall building.
   - Ⓐ It
   - Ⓑ She
   - Ⓒ He

4. We _____ to school.
   - Ⓕ lift
   - Ⓖ pull
   - Ⓗ walk

5. Yesterday we _____ checkers.
   - Ⓐ play
   - Ⓑ played
   - Ⓒ plays

UNIT 9 Being Afraid

Language: Writer's Craft Assessment

Fill in the circle next to the rhyming word to finish the poem.

1. You may very soon,
   take a trip to
   the_____!
   Ⓐ stars
   Ⓑ lake
   Ⓒ moon

2. Where is that goose?
   Oh, it's on the_____!
   Ⓐ fence
   Ⓑ loose
   Ⓒ run

Fill in the circle next to the poem that has the same rhythm as the poem in the box.

> Cat, cat, cat,
> Why are you in the hat?
> Cat, cat, cat,
> Why do you do that?

① Swim, swim,
   To the pool rim,
   Swim, swim,
   Until daylight is dim.

② Bug, bug, bug,
   Why do you cross the
      rug?
   Bug, bug, bug,
   Why are you so smug?

END OF UNIT ASSESSMENT Multiple Choice

UNIT 9 Being Afraid

Oral Fluency Assessment

Kim and the Kitten

Kitten heard a loud noise. He was afraid. He ran under the bed and hid. He did not want to come out.

"I'm sorry," said Kim. She looked under the bed at Kitten. "I dropped my book. Don't be afraid."

Kitten did not understand the little girl. He was still afraid. He did not want to come out from under the bed.

The little girl had an idea. She got a piece of string. The string was Kitten's favorite toy. Quick as a wink, Kitten forgot he was afraid. He wanted to play with the string.

Name _____ Date _____ Score _____

UNIT 9 **Being Afraid**

Listening Assessment

**Listen carefully to each story as it is read to you.
Then fill in the bubble for the best answer.**

1.

 ○    ○    ○

2.

 ○   ○   ○

3.

 ○    ○    ○

4.

 ○    ○    ○

UNIT 9 Being Afraid

Expository Writing Prompt Assessment

Writing Situation
Everyone has something they really like to do on a warm, sunny day.

Audience: Your Classmates

Directions for Writing
Think about one activity you like to do on a warm, sunny day. Then tell how you do this one activity.

Checklist
You will score the most points if you
- Name your activity.
- Tell details about your activity.
- Tell about your activity in order.
- Stay on the topic.
- Use words that tell how you feel.
- Use words that tell what you do.
- Use words that describe.
- Write complete sentences.
- Use correct spelling, capital letters, end marks, and exact words.